Blooming Flc

Coloring Book for Adults

This Coloring Book belongs to:

COLOR TEST

Before you dive into coloring, use this page to test your colors. See how they look on paper, test combinations, or practice your shading and blending techniques to make your coloring experience as enjoyable as possible.

Thank You for Coloring with Us!

We hope "Blooming Flower" has added a touch of color and joy to your days. Your journey through these pages has been a pleasure for us.

If you've enjoyed this floral adventure, please consider leaving a review. Your thoughts and feedback are invaluable in helping us create more beautiful coloring experiences.

Thank you for choosing "Blooming Flower" by DRSM Publishing LLC. May the beauty of flowers continue to inspire you in all your creative endeavors.

With gratitude,
DRSM Publishing LLC

Made in the USA
Middletown, DE
10 November 2024

64286566R00060